Unicorn
TALES

If lost, return to the Rainbow

We have made every effort to ensure that these instructions are accurate and complete. We cannot, however, be responsible for human error, typographical mistakes, or variations in individual work.

Production Team: Concept/Content Developer - Peg Couch, Better Day Books; Technical Editor – Lisa Lancaster; Graphic Artist – Ashley Millhouse; and Prepress – Maddy Ross.

Library of Congress Control Number: 2018965706

Made in U.S.A.

Unicorn
TALES

A Guided Journal for a Magical Life

Contents

Tell the tale of your life!

Come on,
let's get started!

Hello, Cutie!

Do you 💜 unicorns? Of course you do! Everyone loves unicorns. But, why? Sure, they are sparkly and pretty, but the real reason that people love unicorns is because they represent something magical that makes us believe in the impossible. Unicorns make people smile and guess what, so do you! Inside this book, you will have a lot of fun thinking about all the things that make unicorns (and you!) special. You will learn about happiness, individuality, dreams and more. Have fun thinking, writing, drawing and dreaming. Think of this book as your guide to a magical life!

1

Confidence

Confidence is being sure of yourself. It's knowing that you might be a little different than everyone else, but being okay with that! It's believing that you can do hard things, even if you have never done them before. Confidence is a quiet inner strength that lives inside you. It's not loud and boastful. Sometimes confidence can seem more rare than spotting a unicorn! But, it's always there with you.

Just believe.

Always Be
Yourself,

Unless You Can be a
Unicorn

CONFIDENCE

It's easy to remember times when you have been nervous or scared. But, what about all of the times you have felt confident? Write about a memorable time you said to yourself, "I got this!"

Where were you?

_____
_____
_____
_____
_____

What were you doing?

_____
_____
_____
_____
_____

What were you wearing?

_____

_____

_____

_____

_____

_____

How did you feel?
Be sure to use a word other than "confident."

_____

_____

_____

_____

_____

_____

CONFIDENCE

Confidence can be a winding road...

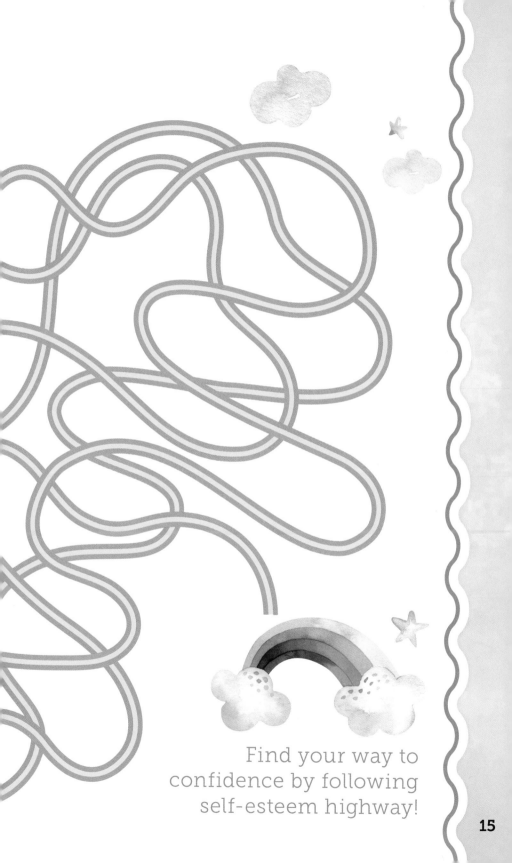

Find your way to confidence by following self-esteem highway!

CONFIDENCE

What makes you feel confident?

List 5 things about yourself that
make you feel confident.

1 _____
_____
_____

2 _____
_____
_____

3 _____
_____
_____

4 _____
_____
_____

5 _____
_____
_____

CONFIDENCE

The opposite of confidence is insecurity.

Feeling insecure is what happens when we question our abilities and compare ourselves to others. Don't worry, everyone feels insecure sometimes, even adults! It's totally normal.

So, how do you turn those insecure feelings around when they sneak up on you? Give yourself a break. Don't be so hard on yourself! Love the things that make you different, focus on doing your best vs. winning, and remember, there is no such thing as perfect!

Read the sentences provided on the next page and then re-write them. Always believe in yourself!

Re-write each sentence.

I am smart.

_____

_____

I am beautiful.

_____

_____

I am kind.

_____

_____

I am loved.

_____

_____

CONFIDENCE

Make a plan for confidence by focusing on the positive everyday.

Write a daily compliment to yourself in the spaces provided. Be sure to read your compliment every morning and re-read it every night. Never stop believing in yourself!

Monday

Tuesday

_____

_____

_____

_____

_____

_____

_____

_____

Wednesday

Thursday

_____

_____

_____

_____

_____

_____

_____

_____

Friday

Saturday

_____

_____

_____

_____

_____

_____

_____

_____

Sunday

_____

_____

Dear me,

_____

_____

_____

_____

_____

_____

_____

_____

_____

_____

_____

_____

_____

_____

_____

_____

_____

_____

_____

_____

_____

_____

_____

_____

_____

_____

_____

_____

_____

_____

_____

_____

_____

_____

_____

_____

xoxo, me

Kindness

What do unicorns represent to you? Sure, they are sparkly and pretty. But, there is more to life than a shiny horn and a rainbow tail (for real!). In addition to being beautiful, unicorns represent kindness...and, that is worth more than all the glitter in the world! Being kind is not the same as being nice. Kindness is what happens when you are truly interested in others. It is what being a seriously good friend is all about. Being kind means taking the time to listen, to laugh, and to learn from each other. Kindness is cool. Be like a unicorn and represent kindness today.

Leave a Trail of

Everywhere
You Go

KINDNESS

Try to remember a time when someone went out of their way to show you kindness.

Who was the person?

_____

_____

_____

_____

_____

_____

How did they show you kindness?

_____

_____

_____

_____

_____

Did their kindness come as a surprise to you?

_____

_____

_____

_____

_____

_____

List three words that describe how their kindness made you feel:

_____

_____

_____

Challenge Yourself to a Kindness Coin Toss

Flip a coin and then select a corresponding "heads" or "tails" act of kindness for the day!

—————————— Day one ——————————

Smile at a stranger.

Give a thank you card to a teacher.

—————————— Day two ——————————

Hug a family member.

Give your BFF a compliment.

Day three

Set the table
for dinner.

☐

Give someone
a high five.

☐

Day four

Offer to help
a neighbor.

☐

Leave a note under a
family member's pillow.

☐

Day five

Donate unused items
to charity.

☐

Hold the door
open for someone.

☐

KINDNESS

Did you complete any of the acts from the Kindness Coin Toss? If yes, good for you! If no, what are you waiting for? Once you have completed your kindness challenge, answer these questions to reflect on your good deed:

Which act did you perform?

_____

_____

_____

_____

_____

_____

Were you hesitant to do it or did you jump in with both feet? Why?

_____

_____

_____

_____

_____

What was the person's reaction and how did it make you feel?

_____

_____

_____

_____

_____

_____

What will your next act of Kindness be?

_____

_____

_____

_____

_____

_____

What does

Kindness

mean to you?

List 5 words that describe kindness.

It's Cool to be Kind

It's super easy to get so busy with our own lives, that we forget to make time for others. Schedule some time this week for kindness. Commit to 4 acts of kindness by writing them down here.

#1:

Kindness Receiver: ———————————————

Kindness Task: ———————————————

When/Where will it happen?: ———————————

———————————————————————

#2:

Kindness Receiver: ———————————————

Kindness Task: ———————————————

When/Where will it happen?: ———————————

———————————————————————

#3:

Kindness Receiver: ————————————————

Kindness Task: ————————————————

When/Where will it happen?: ————————————

————————————————————————————

#4:

Kindness Receiver: ————————————————

Kindness Task: ————————————————

When/Where will it happen?: ————————————

————————————————————————————

Dear me,

xoxo, me

3

Happiness

What makes you happy? Not just a little happy ... but over the rainbow, majestic unicorn kind of happy? Maybe it's hanging out with your best friend and laughing until your belly hurts. Or, maybe it's the warmth and love you feel when you snuggle-up with your pet. Some people are happy when they are super busy and surrounded by lots of excitement. Other people are happy when they are in a quiet space and have time to relax. There is no right or wrong. Each one of us is different, just like the colors of a unicorn!

What do you need to be happy?

Make It a

Rainbow and Unicorn

Kind of Day

HAPPINESS

Think about a recent time when you felt happy.

Where were you?

_____

_____

_____

_____

_____

_____

_____

_____

_____

_____

_____

Why were you happy?

_____

_____

_____

_____

_____

_____

What did that happiness feel like?
List 3 words.

_____

_____

_____

Think Happy Thoughts with a Vision Board

Sometimes it can be hard to explain in words what really makes us happy. Sometimes it's easier to tell our story in pictures. And, a vision board is a great way to get started. A vision board is a collection of photographs, images and memories that remind us of our true happiness. Vision boards can be large or small. Use the space below to create a miniature vision board by taping your items to the page. When you are done, take a moment to review your work. How does it make you feel? Whoops...made you smile!

HAPPINESS

What is one positive thing that you can do right now to feel happiness? Use this page to think of lots of happiness ideas. Then, pick the one thing from the list that you think will bring you the most possible happiness. Use the next page to make a pledge to yourself to do it. Come on, let's get happy!

My Happiness List

1 _____

2 _____

3 _____

4 _____

5 _____

6 _____

7 _____

8 _____

9 _____

10 _____

TIP: Don't think too hard. Just write down 10 ideas that come into your mind as fast as you can!

Ideas: Look at a funny selfie, pet a dog or cat, take a bubble bath, tell someone you love them.

Happiness Pledge:

I _____(write your name) am a huge fan of happiness. I mean, who's not? I have thought of many ways to make myself happy. But, of ALL of the fabulous, amazing, wonderful and brilliant ideas I have come up with...I have picked this one simple thing that I think will make me the happiest! Therefore, I pledge to take action on this item immediately!

_____

_____

_____

(write your idea above)

I believe that even the smallest of actions can make a big difference!

_____

(Sign Here)

HAPPINESS

Now that you have created your miniature Vision Board (you did that, right?!) you probably have a picture in your mind of some things that make you happy. Draw yourself in a happy scene in the space provided. Draw where you are, who you are with, and what is surrounding you. Add a caption below that says what you are thinking.

Draw Here

HAPPINESS

Do you want to know a secret about happiness? It multiplies when it is shared. Spread some positivity today by telling other people what you admire about them. Use the spaces to match a person's name with what you love about them. Be sure to tell them what you think.

Spread the good vibes!

Funniest person I know:

_____

Most stylish person I know:

_____

Most generous person I know:

_____

Most intelligent person I know:

_____

Kindest person I know:

_____

Dear me,

_____

_____

_____

_____

_____

_____

_____

_____

_____

_____

_____

_____

_____

_____

_____

_____

_____

_____

_____

_____

_____

_____

_____

_____

_____

_____

_____

_____

_____

_____

_____

_____

_____

_____

_____

_____

_____

xoxo, me

Faith

Having faith is putting trust in someone
or something outside of yourself. It is
knowing that something is true, even if you
cannot prove it. Faith is believing (not just
a little bit, but with all your heart and soul)
in the things you cannot see. Faith gives
us the confidence to do hard things. Faith
is knowing that everything is going to be
okay. Be like a unicorn and
take a leap today ... but not a leap over
the rainbow, a leap of faith!

Faith gives us wings to fly.

When it Rains,
Look for

Rainbows

When It's Dark
Look for

Stars

FAITH

The saying "leap of faith" means doing something even though you are not sure how it will turn out...like sitting with a bunch of new kids at lunch even though you feel scared to do it. Have you ever taken a leap of faith? Describe what you did and how it turned out.

What is one thing that you did, even though you were scared?

_____

_____

_____

_____

_____

_____

How did you feel right before you did it?

_____

_____

_____

_____

_____

What happened?

_____
_____
_____
_____
_____
_____

How did you feel when it was all over?

_____
_____
_____
_____
_____
_____

FAITH

There is a saying that faith can move mountains. That means that if someone believes in something very strongly, they can do difficult things. What do you believe in strongly? Think about the answer as you color the picture.

FAITH

Faith means different things to different people. What does faith mean to you? Complete the sentences on the next page to discover more about your feelings on faith.

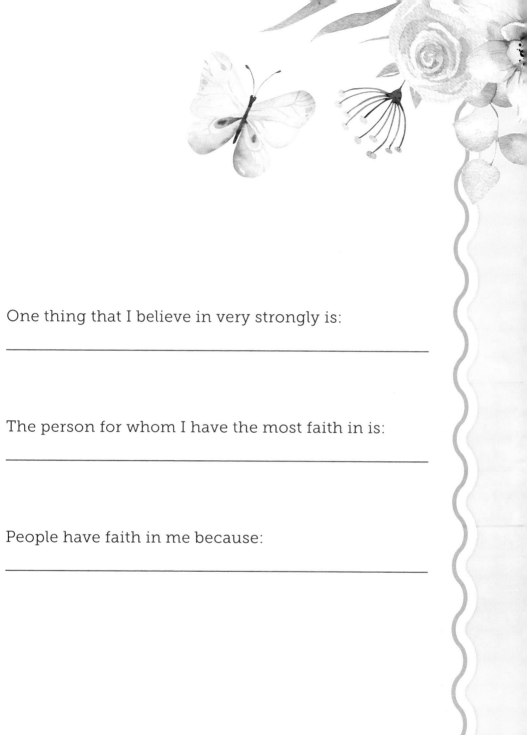

One thing that I believe in very strongly is:

_____

The person for whom I have the most faith in is:

_____

People have faith in me because:

_____

FAITH

Part of faith is seeing the good even when you might feel sad. You can build your faith by focusing on the positive and being grateful. Start a gratitude list to remind yourself of all the wonderful things in your life.

Great things at home:

_____

_____

_____

_____

Great things at school:

_____

_____

_____

_____

_____

_____

My awesome friends:

_____

_____

_____

_____

_____

_____

_____

_____

_____

_____

Things I am grateful for:

_____

_____

_____

_____

_____

_____

Dear me,

_____

_____

_____

_____

_____

_____

_____

_____

_____

_____

_____

_____

_____

_____

_____

_____

_____

_____

_____

_____

xoxo, me

5

Individuality

Individuality is what makes you different
from other people. Sure, you may look
like your mom or have the same sense of
humor as your best friend. But, you are a
true original! Some people think that being
different is a bad thing. But, it's totally
not! Could you imagine if there were no
unicorns ... only horses? How boring!
Be brave, be bold...be YOU.

Embrace Your Inner Unicorn

INDIVIDUALITY

Fitting in is boring. I mean, who wants to be exactly like everyone else? The key to individuality is embracing (or loving) what makes you totally unique. Maybe you have crazy hair, or a really loud laugh. Maybe you dress differently than everyone else or come from a family that's not "perfect". It's all okay! Everyone feels different sometimes. Think about a person that you admire for being different and then answer the questions..

Who do you know that is a true original?

_____

_____

What are the 3 most awesome things about this person?

_____

_____

_____

_____

_____

_____

Do you think that being different makes
this person cool?

_____

_____

_____

_____

_____

_____

What is one thing that makes you unique?

_____

_____

_____

_____

_____

_____

INDIVIDUALITY

What do you think makes you unique? Not just a little different (like different eye or hair color), but what makes you a true individual? Maybe you are an amazing artist or super organized. Maybe you can memorize the words to any song. Maybe you have big ideas that can change the world. Everyone has their own special gifts and talents.

List 6 words that describe you.

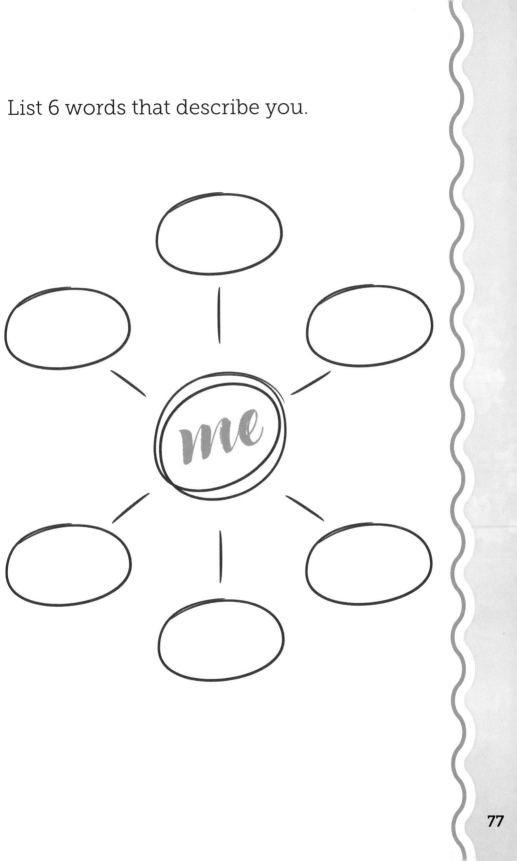

Celebrate your Individuality!

Use the lines provided to describe your fabulous interest, tastes and style.

My favorite song is:

_____

_____

_____

_____

_____

The craziest thing I ever wore was:

_____

_____

_____

_____

_____

The one thing I can do better
than anyone is:

_____

_____

_____

_____

_____

_____

My absolute favorite thing to do is:

_____

_____

_____

_____

_____

_____

INDIVIDUALITY

Sometimes the way you see yourself can be different from the way others see you. Finish the sentences provided and think about the answers. Do the people closest to you know how truly awesome you are? Don't be afraid to show people the real you!

My best friend would describe me as:

_____

_____

_____

_____

_____

_____

My favorite teacher would describe me as:

_____

_____

_____

_____

_____

_____

My family would describe me as:

_____

_____

_____

_____

_____

_____

I describe myself as:

_____

_____

_____

_____

_____

_____

INDIVIDUALITY

You were born to sparkle, shine and jump over rainbows! And, your ideas are a big part of what make you special. Use the boxes provided to list 4 new ideas that inspire you.

1. Style Idea

2. Creative Idea

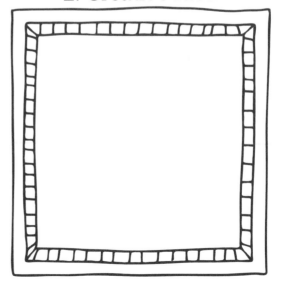

3. Idea to Make the World Better

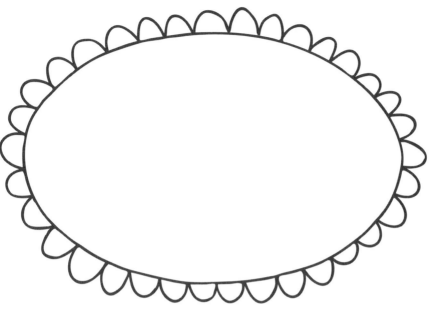

4. Idea to Help Someone

Dear me,

_____

_____

_____

_____

_____

_____

_____

_____

_____

_____

_____

_____

_____

_____

_____

_____

xoxo, me

Creativity

Creativity makes everything fun! Creativity puts color and originality into the world (just like unicorns!). A lot of people think they have to be awesome at art to be "creative". But, that's not true! There are so many ways to be creative. You might be an amazing guitar player or great at decorating. Maybe you love to cook or are super crafty. Some people are creative with their style. There is no one way to be creative. And, guess what the best part about creativity is ... we all have it! Even if you don't know it yet − it's there, inside of you.

You just have to let it out.

Live in a Land of

Make Believe

CREATIVITY

A lot of people say that doing something creative puts them into a super relaxed "zone" of happiness. It feels good to be creative! Can you think of a moment when you were so engrossed in a creative task that time just seemed to slip away? Maybe you were playing an instrument, doing a craft, baking cookies or coloring in a book.

What was the creative activity that you were doing?

_____

_____

_____

_____

What was your favorite part about doing this activity?

_____

_____

_____

_____

_____

Would you like to do this activity again?

_____

_____

_____

_____

_____

_____

Imagine yourself in the future. Can you
think of a job that involves this activity?
What is that job?

_____

_____

_____

_____

_____

_____

CREATIVITY

When it comes to creativity, no two things are the same! Color each of the unicorns in different colors. Give each unicorn a name and make a unicorn family!

CREATIVITY

Creativity and color go together like unicorns and rainbows. Color helps us express our creative ideas. If you could pick any color to paint your room, what color would you choose? We are drawn to certain colors not just because of how they look, but also how they make us feel. Look at the color splashes provided and write one word that describes how that color makes you feel.

Purple

_____

_____

_____

Green

_____

_____

_____

Yellow

_____

_____

_____

Pink

_____

_____

_____

Do One Creative Thing Everyday

If you ask most people if they are creative they will say, "no way", "not me", "nope", or "never going to happen". Well, that's just crazy talk! Everyone is naturally creative. But, creativity does not just magically appear (I mean, we're not unicorns!). You have to practice creativity to build your skills. Use the space provided to practice drawing the same flower everyday for four days. See how your drawing improves as you practice. Don't stop until you are proud!

Day 1

Day 2

Day 3

Day 4

Let Your Light Shine

I am
Creative

Read the sentence inside the heart 3 times.
Repeat as necessary!

Dear me,

_____

_____

_____

_____

_____

_____

_____

_____

_____

_____

_____

_____

_____

_____

_____

_____

_____

_____

xoxo, me

✸ 7 ✸

Magic

Magic, magical, magnificent, marvelous! Sometimes it takes more than one word to describe something so incredibly wonderful that it seems to come from another world. Magical fairy tales, magical unicorns, shooting stars-these are all things that have the ability to make us believe that something big, exciting and beautiful lies just behind the horizon. You can't capture magic, but if you believe hard enough, magic will find you.
Just follow your heart.

Always Believe that

Something

Magical

is Going to
Happen

MAGIC

Magical moments can be great or small. Maybe you went on a fairy tale vacation with your family and had a grand magical experience. Or, maybe you simply found a four-leaf clover on the school playground. It's not the size of the experience that matters, it's how it captures your attention and sparks your imagination. What magical experiences have you had?

What was your experience?

_____

_____

_____

_____

Why was it magical?

_____

_____

_____

_____

_____

_____

What did you hear, see, smell or taste
(include any that apply)?

_____

_____

_____

_____

_____

_____

How did it make you feel?

_____

_____

_____

_____

_____

_____

MAGIC

Wish Upon a Star!

Connect the dots to complete the moon and stars. Color the page when you are complete. While you are coloring, think of 3 wishes and write them down in the space provided.

My 3 Wishes

1 _____

_____

2 _____

_____

3 _____

_____

MAGIC

Magical moments can happen anywhere! Some of the most amazing magical experiences are totally free and found in nature. Have you experienced any of these magical moments? If so, color the star next to it.

Discovered a rainbow.

Found a 4-leaf clover.

Wished on a shooting star.

Caught a firefly.

MAGIC

Where can you let your imagination wander? Is it outside in nature or maybe inside, lying on your bed and listening to music? Have you found magic and imagination in a cool secret hideaway, like a treehouse or fort? Imagine yourself inside the beautiful tent pictured on this page. What are you thinking about? Close your eyes and dream. What do you see? How do you feel?

Write your vision down in the clouds.

MAGIC

Make Your Own Magic

Imagination, play and curiosity are the keys to magic. Take some time every day to get out and explore. Let's be real, you might not see a unicorn. But, you just might see a falling star, a flock of birds, or a deer in the woods. Record your observations in the space provided. And always remember, magic is all around you.

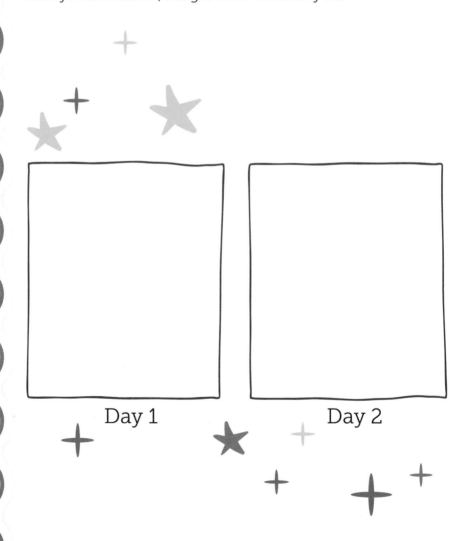

Day 1

Day 2

Day 3

Day 4

Day 5

Day 6

Dear me,

_____

_____

_____

_____

_____

_____

_____

_____

_____

_____

_____

_____

_____

_____

_____

_____

_____

_____

_____

xoxo, me

Wishes

Close your eyes and make a wish. Go on, right now. Take a deep breath. Count to three. Then, (1-2-3) make your wish! What did you wish for? Did you know ahead of time what your wish would be or did it just pop into your brain? Wishes are funny little things. We may not think about them, but they are always with us. Wishes are like unicorns, they allow us to dream the impossible. Wishes can be as grand as your mind can imagine. Wishes remind us of our heart's deepest desire.
Wishes can come true.

Never Stop Looking Up

WISHES

Wishing is an important part of dreaming. Wishes allows us to believe that something wonderful is going to happen. Do you make a wish every year when you blow out your birthday candles? Have you ever wished upon a star? Think about all of the wishes you have made as you answer these questions.

What is the one thing you wish for most often?

_____

_____

_____

_____

_____

_____

Have any of your wishes ever come true yet? If so, which one(s)?

_____

_____

_____

_____

_____

_____

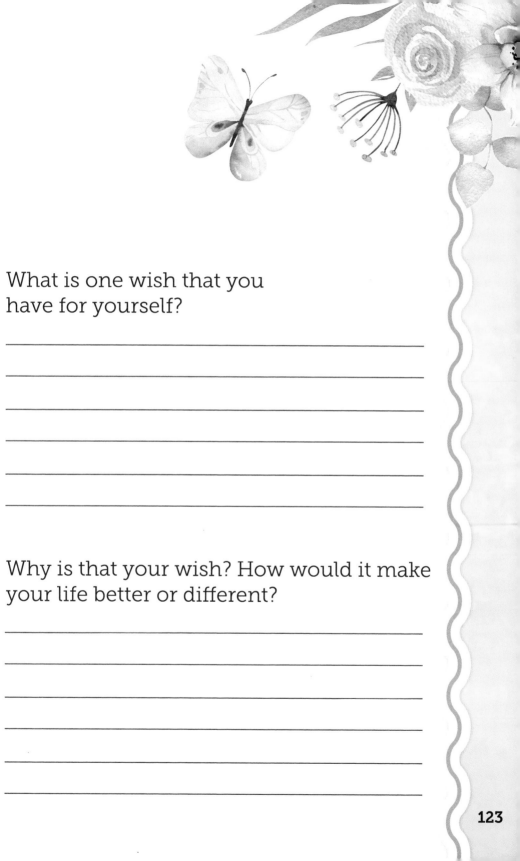

What is one wish that you
have for yourself?

_____

_____

_____

_____

_____

_____

Why is that your wish? How would it make
your life better or different?

_____

_____

_____

_____

_____

_____

WISHES

Make a Wish

You don't have to wait until your birthday to make a wish! Wishes are good for us and help us to express our deepest desires. Pretend it is your birthday. Close your eyes and blow (really hard) on the candle pictured. Now, wait and see if your wish comes true.

Close your eyes and blow on the candle!

WISHES

Legend has it that if you rub a brass lamp, a genie will appear and you will be granted three wishes. Rub the lamp provided and then record one wish for yourself, one wish for your family and one wish for the world.

You will be granted 3 wishes:

Wish for me:

_____

_____

Wish for my family:

_____

_____

Wish for the world:

_____

_____

WISHES

There are so many wishing traditions from around the world. People in the Philippines make a wish when they see lightning strike. In Japan, wishes are made when catching a falling leaf. In many European countries wishes are made by throwing coins into a fountain. Can you think of a new wishing tradition? Use the prompts provided to think of other ideas:

Every time I see a

_____

I will make a wish.

Every time

_____

giggles I will make a wish.

My own wish tradition:

_____

_____

_____

_____

How to Wish into a Fountain:

Stand backwards and throw three coins. With each toss make the same wish. If you hear three splashes as your coins hit the water, your wish will come true!

Be a Well Wisher!

Wishes are not just for yourself. You can wish great things for your friends, family, teachers, neighbors and the world! Use the wish list provided to write down the wishes you have for others.

Wish List for Others

_____

_____

_____

_____

_____

_____

_____

_____

_____

Dear me,

xoxo, me

Dreams

There are two kinds of dreams. The dreams you dream at night, and the dreams that live in your heart and soul. The dreams that come from your heart and soul are ideas that you can't get out of your head. They keep poking you over and over...like a unicorn horn! Maybe you have a dream to sing a solo at the next chorus concert. Or, maybe you have a dream that you will be a fabulous fashion designer, or an amazing veterinarian that helps saves animals. Whatever your dream is, always remember that it is yours!

Never stop believing!

Everything
You Can

Imagine

is Real

DREAMS

Dreams are wishes that you can't let go. They just kind of keep hanging around! They are pretty persistent and demand your attention. And, isn't that wonderful? Be sure to listen to your dreams so you can make them a reality. Use the prompts below to help identify your dreams.

When I grow up, my dream job would be:

_____

_____

_____

_____

_____

_____

I can make the world a better place by:

_____

_____

_____

_____

_____

_____

I dream of visiting the following places:

_____
_____
_____
_____
_____
_____

My dream day includes:

_____
_____
_____
_____
_____
_____

DREAMS

Dream Log

Sometimes the dreams you dream at night can have clues to your heart dreams. Keep a log of your dreams on these pages. Just write down one thing that you remember from your night dream. It's amazing to see what your mind can think of when you're asleep!

Day Dreaming

Dreams are big ideas and dreams can (and have!) changed the world. But, it's also great to have smaller dreams about the everyday things in our life. These are sometimes called day dreams. On these pages, spend some time day dreaming about your future dream house. What does it look like? What color would you decorate it? What style would all of your furniture be? Do you like any of the items shown below and can you see them in your house? Circle any that you like and then draw your future dream house.

Draw Here

Don't Be Afraid to Let Your Mind Wander

Where does your mind go when you're not busy with school, studying or doing activities? It's good to give your brain a rest so your dreams have time to pop out and say, "hello!"

Take a few moments to clear your mind. Focus on your breathing as you look at the beautiful feathers on the next page. Breathe in, breathe out. Look at the detail in the pictures. Try to keep your focus for 3 minutes.

Ah...life is beautiful when we take a moment to rest!

Clear your mind so your dreams have a place to grow!
Focus on your breathing as you look at the feathers
for 3 minutes. Rest, relax, and dream.

DREAMS

If you can dream it, you can do it!

It's never to early to start preparing for your dreams to come true. In the space provided, list one dream (your biggest!) and then add 5 things that you can do today to start living your dream. For example, if you dream of visiting France one day, you can start by learning how to say a few words in French, cooking a French recipe, or learning fun facts about France's capital, Paris. The more we focus on our dreams, the more prepared we are to realize them!

My Dream:

_____

_____

_____

_____

_____

How to start living my dream:

1 _____
_____

2 _____
_____

3 _____
_____

4 _____
_____

5 _____
_____

Dear me,

_____

_____

_____

_____

_____

_____

_____

_____

_____

_____

_____

_____

_____

_____

_____

_____

_____

_____

_____

xoxo, me

10

Giggles

Okay, so unicorns are inspirational,
beautiful and other worldly. But, seriously –
they are just so darn cute that they make us
smile. Unicorns are playful, colorful, shiny
and don't take themselves too seriously.
Let's lighten up and be more like unicorns.
Because after all, there's nothing better
than a good belly laugh...except maybe a
unicorn belly laugh.

Unicorn vibes = good vibes!

The
Unicorns
Made Me
Do It!

GIGGLES

Have you ever had the giggles so bad that you thought you might get in trouble?! LOL. It happens to everyone at some point in time. Maybe you were in class, in church or being lectured by someone and something (usually provoked by your best friend) just made you crack up. And, knowing that you were not supposed to laugh only makes you laugh harder. Tell about the time:

I got the giggles so bad one time.
It happened at (name the place):

_____

_____

_____

_____

I was with (name the people):

_____

_____

_____

_____

_____

_____

The part that was so funny was:

_____

_____

_____

_____

_____

_____

Everytime I think about _____

_____

I still giggle.

GIGGLES

What do you get when you mix a unicorn with an adorable kitty? A cat-i-corn, duh! Caticorns might be the only thing that can rival the cuteness of a unicorn. Experience giggles and a cuteness overload as you color the caticorns on the next page!

Dear me,

_____

_____

_____

_____

_____

_____

_____

_____

_____

_____

_____

_____

_____

_____

_____

_____

_____

_____

_____

_____

xoxo, me

The End